THE

MACKINAC BRIDGE STORY

BY PRENTISS M. BROWN

DETROIT   WAYNE UNIVERSITY PRESS   1956

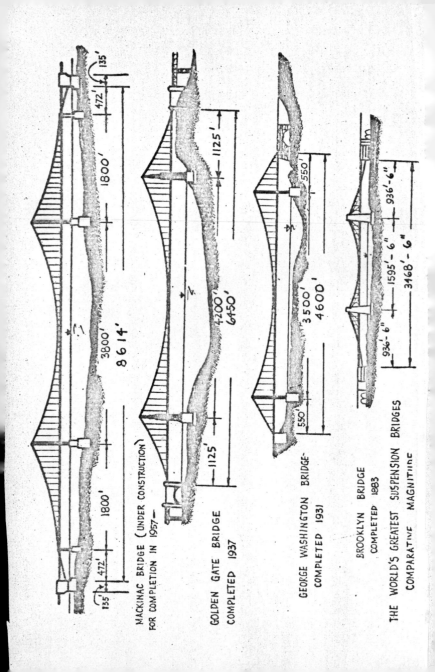

135' 472' 1800' 3800' 1800' 472' 135'

8614'

MACKINAC BRIDGE (UNDER CONSTRUCTION)
FOR COMPLETION IN 1957—

1125' 4200' 1125'

6450'

GOLDEN GATE BRIDGE
COMPLETED 1937

550' 3500' 550'

4600'

GEORGE WASHINGTON BRIDGE-
COMPLETED 1931

936'-6" 1595'-6" 936'-6"

3468'-6"

BROOKLYN BRIDGE
COMPLETED 1883

THE WORLD'S GREATEST SUSPENSION BRIDGES
COMPARATIVE MAGNITUDE

That was the day Prentiss Brown became a Democrat. Any Republican want to rise to a point of order?

George W. Stark
Detroit Historiographer

PREFACE

The printed page cannot tell the story of the terrific struggle to achieve the result accomplished in the financing of the Mackinac Bridge. Public sentiment had to be aroused in the heavily populated parts of the state to favor the expenditure of a huge sum of money in a sparsely settled area. No large cities were located nearby the bridgeheads. The traffic is seasonal to a considerable extent. Advocates of the ferry system were opposed. A new boat was under construction. Ice, wind, alleged bad rock conditions, deep water, currents, and other adverse factors were cited. The trend of the time was against public expenditures. Nearby financial institutions, such as some of the Mid-West insurance companies, were skeptical. The bonds were not eligible for Michigan bank investment. Interest rates were on an upward trend. Twice we tried and twice we failed. We in the Authority felt much as did General Foch at the Battle of the Marne in 1914 when he is reported to have said, "My right is in retreat, my left is shattered, my center is

wavering: I order that the offensive be renewed." Well, we got the money.

I cannot too highly commend my fellow members of the Authority. Fred Zeder has passed on. He was an enthusiast for the project from the beginning and a mighty factor in our success. He was succeeded by Mead Bricker, who ably took his place. Two outstanding Michigan men from the automobile industry whose drive, effective there, was productive in this effort. George Osborn and Bill Cochran from the Northern Peninsula, ever sure in attendance, who know well the need and feel certain of the success of the bridge, were most helpful. Mr. Osborn handled publicity, his "Sault News" and radio station WSOO covering much of the northern area, and Mr. Cochran spoke extensively throughout the area, both with splendid results. Governor Van Wagoner in his administration advanced the cause and watched our interests in the contract negotiations. His experience in highway contracting was vital in these decisions. Commissioner Ziegler and his aide, George Foster, who usually sat for the commissioner, gave counsel and supplied statistics for the traffic and bridge engineers. Finally, Mr. Fisher, whose work on the Finance Committee and as vice-chairman, based on his extensive financial contacts, opened the doors for us wherever we went in the money mazes of Wall Street. His standing and prestige and his devotion to the task were major factors in our final success.

All subjects dealing with Authority business were thoroughly discussed and often differences of opinion

arose; however, in the final voting, the vote always was unanimous on the part of all members present.

Our engineer, David B. Steinman, is among the world's greatest, and with his staff has been a major factor in all phases, not only in design and construction but in financing and publicity. He has been ably aided by Glenn B. Woodruff, his associate.

We are fortunate in having as our contractors Merritt-Chapman and Scott Corporation and the American Bridge Division of the United States Steel Corporation, leaders throughout the world in this type of work.

The Authority secured as its executive secretary Lawrence A. Rubin of Lansing, who has been a tower of strength in the struggle to bring about the success of the project. In the legislative effort, the sale of the bonds, and in the contract negotiations, he has been a constant aid to us.

Three Michigan corporations, the National Bank of Detroit, the Chrysler Corporation and the Detroit Edison Company, loaned such of their facilities as were requested by the Authority. Top men in these devoted much time to the effort. They joined in building the bridge model, shown throughout the state, and aided much in arousing pro-bridge sentiment.

Governor Williams promised the people to do something about the bridge, created the Inter-Peninsula Communications Commission referred to in the lecture, and constantly urged action. His leadership has been a major factor in our success.

The Legislature was controlled by the Republican party. The governor was a Democrat. The leaders of both parties were confronted by some opposition in their ranks. However, wise counsel prevailed and the passage of the various bills necessary to the project were handled without partisanship.

One cannot mention all who made major contributions, and I regret this, but I am sure such an attempted list would leave out many, because hundreds in the Legislature and out worked on the project through its many phases; so I must content myself with what has been said here and in the Cass Lecture.

P. M. B.

The Mackinac Bridge Story

THE LEWIS CASS LECTURES

Publication of this booklet was made possible by the
financial assistance of the Detroit Historical Society Guild

THE CASS LECTURESHIP

In 1948 the trustees of the Detroit Historical Society on the recommendation of the president, Dr. Alfred H. Whittaker, approved the naming of a committee to plan an annual program to be known as the Cass Lecture and to select a speaker who would present to the Society a subject of current or historical interest and significance. Dr. David D. Henry, Monsignor Edward J. Hickey, and Marquis E. Shattuck were appointed to the committee. The first lecture, an appraisal of the life and signal service to Detroit of Father Gabriel Richard, was presented by Stanley Pargellis, librarian of the Newberry Library in Chicago.

In succeeding years, historians and historically-minded men whom the Society has sought to honor have delivered scholarly lectures which the Society has published for distribution to its members. The seventh of these annual lectures was given on the evening of May 25, 1955, in the Hall of Industry of the Detroit Historical Museum, by the Honorable Prentiss M. Brown, president of the Society from

1953 to 1955. His presentation was in the tradition of the Historical Society of Michigan, the first historical organization of the old Northwest Territory. In September 1829, the members of that Society called upon their president, Lewis Cass, the distinguished governor of the Territory, to address the membership on the first anniversary of the formation of the Society. The address on that occasion was subsequently published and is now an invaluable item in the archives of Michigan. In like manner, the Detroit Historical Society seeks to foster historical research and encourage the preparation of manuscripts for publication which will prove valued additions to the public historical libraries of this area and to the private collections of its members.

Marquis E. Shattuck
Chairman
Cass Lectureship Committee

FOREWORD

A Michigan legislator with a gift for metaphor said when the bill was passed to bring the Mackinac Bridge into reality, "The North and the South of the state have long been engaged; they now have a wedding ring." Such being the case, there is every reason to refer to Prentiss Marsh Brown, chairman of the Mackinac Bridge Authority, as a member of the wedding.

All will agree, I think, that Mr. Brown has been the most important member of the wedding between the Northern and the Southern peninsulas. And since this slender volume contains his own modest recapitulation of the fascinating story of the financing of the world's greatest bridge, let us give some consideration to the man whose enthusiasm and sense of history brought it to focus and to a successful issue.

The bridge, even before it takes solid shape before us, most certainly must be accounted the most spectacular of his achievements. At least, that is the way he now regards it. Already Michigan people are referring to him as "Mr. Bridge," and he doesn't object, even though the designation brushes off some notable past performances: a political career that carried him from prosecuting attorney of Mackinac County to the chairmanship of Michigan Democratic State conventions over a period of years; to a seat in Congress from the Eleventh District, the first Democrat ever to represent that rock-ribbed Republican area; to the United States Senate, where he became a trouble-shooter for Franklin D. Roosevelt; to head of the Office of Price Administration; to the chairmanship of the board of the Detroit Edison Company; to honorary posts in various fields of business and of culture, too numerous to catalog here.

So he rejoices in the name of "Mr. Bridge."

The researcher may find in Mr. Brown's life ample reason why he should, since the very circumstances of his birth indicated a Great Lakes direction. He was born in St. Ignace and is probably the only citizen of Michigan whose entry into the world caused his small corner of it to cease its normal operations and, in a manner of speaking, to call out a holiday.

His father, James J. Brown, was prosecuting attorney of Mackinac County at the time. Naturally, Judge J. H. Steere, of the Eleventh Judicial Circuit, adjourned court and the new little citizen was made the subject of an official manifesto. Prosecutor Brown went home to tell his new son the news and to point out to him the advantages of a home site that overlooked the majestic straits with the long ships passing.

So Prentiss Brown was singled out by destiny from the beginning. He grew into a man who not only had a deep consciousness of history but a way of making it himself. His concern with it brought him to the presidency of the Detroit Historical Society and the presidency of the Michigan Historical Commission.

Also, the researcher may delve into the early life and deeds of Mr. Bridge and find basic reasons for other directions his lively career has taken. Politics, for instance.

Prentiss Brown cherishes an old photograph, which shows Detroit's official family moving from the old City Hall at the head of Cadillac Square into another City Hall across Woodward, which only recently was abandoned in favor of the monumental City-County Building. Prominent in this group is his father, who was then the city attorney, a post now recognized as corporation counsel. All the marchers are distinguished by Prince Albert coats and tall silk hats. All, that is, but Town Lawyer Brown. He's wearing a jaunty straw, a true non-conformist.

The Browns moved north and in that enchanted country, Prentiss lived out an average American boyhood. This led him to a bellhop's job in a Mackinac Island hotel.

One day an important delegation from Washington, D.C., landed there. Prentiss struggled with the luggage of the more impressive guests—up two flights of stairs. When he looked at the tip, he found it scarcely adequate. For Vice-President Fairbanks had given him but one thin dime.

THE MACKINAC BRIDGE STORY

AS FAR BACK AS three generations ago Michigan citizens had varying opinions about a bridge or tunnel at the Straits of Mackinac. Thomas T. Bates, editor-publisher of the "Grand Traverse Herald," wrote in the early winter of 1884 that "if there is to be a great through route from east to west through Michigan there must be a sure and permanent crossing at the Straits." Mr. Bates' comment was pertinent enough to be reprinted in the "Lansing Tri-Weekly Republican" of February 5, 1884. While the emphasis in the news item was on the fact that the experiment to provide year-round steamboat transportation across the Straits had failed (actually, the great ice-crusher "St. Ignace" was built, and with its successors the "Ste. Marie" and the "Chief Wawatam," designed by the Detroit marine architect Frank E. Kirby, gave excellent rail ferry service and continue to do so now), the article was accurately prophetic in stating the real problem of the Mackinac Bridge: "The important question is, will the business to be done warrant the expenditure of the large amount of money required in the building of such a bridge or the construction of a tunnel under the Straits."

From 1884 to 1920 the idea of a connecting link at the Straits cropped up in many places, and in 1920 an article in "American Highways" by Horatio "Good Roads" Earle, Michigan's first state highway commissioner, created more than passing interest. He suggested a floating tunnel at the Straits of Mackinac and invited his engineering colleagues to comment thereon. Early in 1921, Charles Evan Fowler of New York City made a counter-proposal to build a series of causeways and bridges beginning at a point near Cheboygan across to Bois Blanc Island, to Round Island, over the west tip of Mackinac Island, and then across the channel to St. Ignace.

Nothing came of these proposals at the time, but in response to the growing demand for better Straits crossing facilities, Governor Alex J. Groesbeck urged the Legislature in 1923 to establish a ferry service. This was done. In 1928 the Highway Department published a report stating that a bridge directly across the Straits costing about $30,000,000 would be feasible as a private toll facility. Although some steps were taken to carry out this proposal, they were not completed and the project was abandoned.

Spurred by the depression and the availability of work project funds from the Federal government and urged by Governor William A. Comstock, the Legislature in 1934 created the Mackinac Straits Bridge

Authority to investigate the feasibility of a bridge, issue and sell bonds, build a bridge, and fix and collect tolls. The enabling act was presented by Representative Edward H. Fenlon of the Mackinac-Emmett district (then my law partner, now Circuit Judge for the counties of Emmett, Cheboygan and Mackinac) where the bridgeheads are located.

Stephen T. Stackpole of Detroit, Otto W. Lang of Mackinac Island, and Patrick H. Kane of Port Huron were appointed members of the Authority by Governor Comstock in April, 1934. It was thought the railroads would be interested, and Mr. Stackpole, who was a leading railroad executive in the state, was made a member for that reason. The Authority retained Charles Evan Fowler as temporary chief engineer and me as legal advisor. Fowler's original island hopping plan was revised slightly and in August of 1934 was submitted to the Public Works Administration with a request for a loan of 70 per cent and a grant of 30 per cent to finance the estimated cost of the project, about $35,000,000.

In the meantime, considerable objection to the island route developed throughout the state. With many others I was never in agreement with Fowler. While the crossing from the south mainland southeast of Cheboygan to Bois Blanc Island is comparatively shallow, it is about five miles long over navigable water in constant use by shipping. In addition the proposed route involved a twelve mile road on the island and two water jumps from Bois Blanc to Round and Mackinac islands, the latter over a major

5

shipping passage, and finally the main bridge structure from Mackinac Island to St. Ignace, about as long and with as many problems as the direct route now adopted from Mackinaw City to St. Ignace. It was felt to be entirely impracticable. Mr. Fowler constantly urged me when I was in Congress to support this route but met with no success.

While the Authority considered revising its application to cover a direct route from Mackinaw City to St. Ignace, as recommended by Professor James H. Cissell of the University of Michigan, on July 18, 1935, the request for funds for the Fowler route was denied, and Mr. Fowler's services were discontinued. However, the Authority was informed that the denial of its original application would not prejudice an amended application covering a new route.

Francis C. McMath, former chief engineer for the Canadian Bridge Company, was engaged by the Authority to prepare the data for a new application covering the direct route bridge. Professor Cissell was engaged as consulting engineer. The Authority contracted to obtain borings and after much difficulty only two rock samples were obtained at designated points along the proposed route. On September 7, 1935 a new application for a loan and grant was filed with the Public Works Administration.

By this time the project had been well publicized due largely to the activities of the late Governor Chase S. Osborn. With me he interested President Roosevelt in the project and the latter ordered the Army Corps of Engineers to report on the location, prelim-

6

inary estimate of cost, general feasibility and necessity of the proposed structure. The report was favorable to the direct route, and the project was considered entirely feasible (providing additional foundation data were obtained), of unquestionable great
public convenience, and financially reasonable.

Notwithstanding this report and tremendous support from citizens and citizen groups from all parts of
Michigan, the application for a loan and grant of funds
was denied by the Works Progress Administration on
September 18, 1936.

The state Highway Department at this point pro-
ceeded to improve the ferry service by purchasing and
rehabilitating railroad ferries that were no longer
being used in trans-lake service. However, because
of the ferry operation cost, the ever increasing demand for service and the inability of boats to supply
such service on a satisfactory basis, the highway commissioner, Murray D. Van Wagoner, became vitally
interested in the bridge project. His chief deputy, G.
Donald Kennedy, was appointed chairman of the
Mackinac Straits Bridge Authority, and a new chapter
in linking the two peninsulas began.

The Authority began negotiations with the long-
span-bridge engineering firm of Modjeski and Masters
in 1937. By the end of the next year an agreement
had been made with this firm to provide the Authority with preliminary plans for a structure across the
Straits. It provided for the Authority to furnish the
engineers with considerable data along the route selected. In cooperation with the Highway Department

7

surveys of several routes were made and finally a straight line from Mackinaw City almost due north to a point in the southwest corner of St. Ignace was selected. Soundings and borings were taken along this line, traffic data were obtained, geological studies were made, and all the information turned over to Modjeski and Masters, who filed a preliminary report in June of 1940.

The report called for the construction along the aforementioned line of a double suspension span, one of which would be the world's longest at 4,600 feet. It also called for a causeway from St. Ignace 4,200 feet south into shallow water. It recommended that this causeway be used as a fair-weather ferry boat dock during bridge construction, thereby shortening the trip and increasing the ferry capacity without any additional investment in ships. It estimated that the structure would cost $24,340,000. Both Leon S. Moisseiff, internationally famous bridge designer, and James Cissell endorsed the report.

The Highway Department let a contract for the construction of the causeway, which was completed in 1941. But the outbreak of World War II put an end to work on the bridge by the Mackinac Straits Bridge Authority, and the state Legislature abolished the Authority in 1947. Soon thereafter funds were appropriated to construct a double ended ice-breaker ferry that would carry 150 vehicles. Plans for a new dock at St. Ignace to shorten the ferry sailing time were drafted, and it was expected that these measures

would take care of the foreseeable demand for Straits crossing service.

Others saw the situation differently and in 1948 Governor G. Mennen Williams created the Inter-Peninsula Communications Commission. One of the functions of this commission, headed by the chairman of Michigan's Public Service Commission, John H. McCarthy, was to explore the possibility of a connecting link at the Straits.

Shortly thereafter, W. Stewart Woodfill, president of the Grand Hotel on Mackinac Island, interested a group of leading businessmen from all parts of the state to join with him in a Mackinac Bridge Citizens Committee. The immediate objective of this committee was to secure creation of another Mackinac Bridge Authority to finance and build a bridge after thoroughly investigating its feasibility.

The efforts of both these bodies along with constant prodding by Governor Williams brought partial results in 1950 with the Legislature's creation of the Mackinac Bridge Authority, limited, however, to studies of feasibility with no power whatsoever to finance and build. Governor Williams appointed six of a seven man commission, to serve without compensation, comprised of three Democrats and three Republicans and the state highway commissioner, who was named a member in the legislation creating the Authority. The members took their oaths of office on June 6, 1950. They were Fred M. Zeder (now deceased and his vacancy filled by Mead L. Bricker), Charles T. Fisher, Jr., George A. Osborn, Murray D.

Van Wagoner, William J. Cochran, state Highway Commissioner Charles M. Ziegler and I. Shortly thereafter, the Michigan Senate unanimously confirmed these appointments.

Public Act Number 21 of the Public Acts of 1950 creating the Mackinac Bridge Authority carefully spelled out the Authority's functions. First, it was to determine physical feasibility. Could a structure actually be built at the Straits of Mackinac that would withstand all the forces of nature in that area: the winds, the ice, the currents, the depths of water and the allegedly unsafe rock under the Straits? Second, it was to determine costs. Could such a structure be build at a reasonable cost? In other words, could it be self-liquidating? The act provided an appropriation of $100,000 to cover the expense.

To obtain the answers to these questions the Authority was ordered by the Legislature to consult with a board of three of the world's greatest long-span-bridge engineers. These consultants were to be selected at the recommendation of the Dean of Engineering of the University of Michigan. Meeting at the Straits of Mackinac on June 24, 1950, the Authority invited the three top men on Dean Crawford's list: O. H. Ammann and D. B. Steinman of New York City, and Glenn B. Woodruff of San Francisco. On July 12, these three men came to the Straits and accepted the commission to advise the Authority on the physical feasibility of a bridge and its probable cost. The act creating the Authority specified that none of the engineers retained to determine feasibility

10

could eventually be retained to design the bridge. The purpose of this provision was to eliminate the temptation to file a favorable report in the hope of obtaining the assignment to draw the final plans. I did not like this provision. Men of character in the profession would not be affected by thought of personal gain.

Next, the Authority entered into an agreement with the traffic engineering firm of Coverdale and Colpitts of New York City, recognized for their ability to predict traffic on toll facilities such as bridges, turnpikes, terminals and similar projects. While the design engineers were developing their report the traffic analysts were conducting interviews at the Straits of Mackinac and in other areas from where traffic mainly originated and to where it was going.

Finally, on January 10, 1951 the Authority received preliminary reports from Messrs. Ammann, Steinman and Woodruff, and from the firm of Coverdale and Colpitts. The former said in effect that a bridge could be built connecting Michigan's two peninsulas along the direct straight route from Mackinaw City north and utilizing the causeway built in 1941, that it would withstand all the physical forces in the area, that additional borings would be required before the precise location of each foundation could be determined, and that such a structure was estimated to cost $76,300,000.

The Authority retained the services of two expert consulting geologists. It had been alleged that there were huge caverns in and under the rock on which the foundations would be placed and consequently the structure would be in jeopardy because the weight of the foundations would cause the caverns to collapse, thus bringing the bridge down on top of them. The consulting geologists, Sidney Paige and Charles P. Berkey, studied the problem and filed a report stating that the so-called caverns had collapsed thousands of years ago and had consolidated into rock.

The Coverdale and Colpitts report stated that such a structure could be financed by selling bonds, the interest and principal on which would be paid for out of tolls based upon those charged for crossing by ferry. It was estimated such financing would cost about $11,000,000, thereby requiring a total sale of $87,000,000 worth of bonds.

The question of putting a railroad on the bridge was discussed by the engineers, and an estimate of $60,000,000 additional was made. This matter was discussed with prominent railroad men, and it was felt that the interest and payment of the bonds would be a heavier charge than the cost of operation of the ferry system long used by the railroad companies. Nothing further was done along this line.

The Authority promptly filed the reports with the Legislature but did not recommend additional legislation at this time since it was impossible to obtain steel without a certificate of necessity indicating that the project was for the purpose of civilian defense. However, the Authority was granted an additional $75,000 to proceed with its investigation of feasibility, particularly in connection with the bearing

qualities of the rock on which the foundations would rest.

Load bearing tests were carried out during the early winter of 1951. They were made on material at the Straits that was deemed the weakest of all found in the area. It was concluded from these tests that this weakest of all the rock at the Straits would support four times the full load placed on it by the bridge foundations.

By late 1951 and early 1952 the steel situation had eased sufficiently for the Authority to proceed. Two bills were drafted for consideration by the Legislature. One bill simply appropriated $2,000,000 out of highway funds for the purpose of engaging an engineer to draw final plans for the structure. It gave the Authority no right to finance or build, but merely to obtain plans.

The second bill, which was the primary objective of the Authority, covered all the powers necessary for financing and constructing a bridge. The Legislature refused the use of highway funds for bridge plans but promptly enacted the complete enabling legislation, with one amendment. The section appropriating $40,000 to the Authority to accomplish the bridge financing and construction was amended to appropriate one dollar for these purposes. This made a total of $175,001 appropriated to the Authority, of which over $24,000 was subsequently returned.

The next task was to persuade the Legislature to authorize the Authority to proceed with financing and construction. I presented our case to a joint

13

session of the Senate and the House and with our engineers submitted to questions by the legislators. We submitted a bill which we had drafted. It authorized us to bond and build if it could be done without state guaranty of the bonds. We also asked that since the restriction against the use of the engineers had served its purpose and since they were best informed by their investigation, they be considered for design engineers for the project. The Legislature was favorably impressed by Messrs. Ammann, Steinman, and Woodruff, and the restriction was eliminated.

After several months of committee study and floor discussion, and many conferences with the Authority, the Legislature passed this bill by more than two-thirds majorities in both houses. It was given immediate effect and the Governor signed it into Public Act No. 214 of the Public Acts of 1952, on April 30, 1952.

The Authority immediately filed an application with the Reconstruction Finance Corporation for that agency to purchase the bonds to be issued by the Authority.

While the RFC was investigating the application, traffic at the Straits was increasing at a rate far greater than that predicted by the traffic analysts. Instead of the 6 per cent a year increase in 1951 and 1952, the trend was better than 15 per cent a year. This encouraged private investment bond bankers to

become interested in the project, and the Authority requested the RFC to hold its application in abeyance.

Careful consideration was given to the question of Reconstruction Finance Corporation or private financing. There was a general nationwide sentiment that the RFC should curtail its operations; an election was on and a change in Administration probable. The Authority, through Mr. Fisher, requested an expert bond financier, Milton S. Bosley of the National Bank of Detroit, to report on the possible RFC proposition and an alternative under discussion. The private financing looked a little more favorable from Mr. Bosley's figures. At that time the RFC interest charge was 4¼ per cent, and the proposal by the underwriter was 4 per cent. There had always been a strong feeling on the part of the Authority that the bridge project should stand on its own, without Federal funds if possible.

In November, 1952 the Authority entered into an agreement with a leading New York revenue bond underwriter to manage the bridge financing, selected D. B. Steinman as designing engineer, and recommended Glenn B. Woodruff as consulting engineer. Tentative contracts contingent upon successful financing were entered into for the substructure and the superstructure. All the necessary legal and financing documents were prepared and the Authority was ready to market its bonds in late March, 1953. By that time, the money market which had been tightening up steadily since the first of the year was unable to absorb the $96,000,000* bridge revenue bond issue, and financing was postponed.

Members of the Authority and others had pointed out to the traffic engineers that the ferry operation was suffering heavy operating losses, reaching figures considerably over half a million dollars annually, without consideration of the interest or depreciation on the docks and ships. Consequently, the traffic engineers recommended that the Authority request the Legislature to appropriate a similar amount annually to pay the cost of operating, repairing and maintaining the bridge. This would make the sale of the bonds more attractive, since all revenues produced by the structure would be available for the payment of interest and liquidation of bonds.

In May, 1953 an act was passed appropriating $417,000 a year for that purpose, if and when the structure was opened to traffic. It took an immense amount of effort to bring this result about. Mr. Fisher, former Governor Van Wagoner, other members of the Authority and I made many trips to consult with various legislative committees and groups. Governor Williams, both party leaders, and many

*The difference between this figure and the $87,000,000 previously mentioned is due to an interest factor, the interest having to be figured on two bases. (Rates also had gone up slightly.) As a governmental agency, the RFC could pay out the money when needed on the contracts for construction. Investment bankers cannot do this on non-state guaranty bonds; they must know that all the money is subscribed and in hand so that the project can be completed. Hence, interest on the total amount had to be included in the figure and paid during construction.

others urged the action, and it was finally taken. The Legislature put a time limit on this offer so that unless the bonds were sold by December 31, 1953, the $417,000 would be withdrawn.

Another effort was planned for June, 1953, and it likewise was called off because of bond market conditions. The summer months saw no improvement in financial circles and it was not until mid-autumn that some encouragement appeared. In the early fall, Mr. Fisher and I spent considerable time calling upon insurance company executives and bond underwriters in New York, Montreal, Chicago and Milwaukee trying to interest them in financing the Mackinac Bridge. The first encouraging result from this effort was a trip made by Stuart Silloway, financial vice-president of the Mutual Life of New York, who drove up to the Bridge locality and satisfied himself that the project had real merit from a financial standpoint. He so advised Mr. Fisher and indicated that his company would give careful consideration to a $2 million participation.

Meanwhile, James S. Abrams, Jr., a New York investment banker with Allen and Company, proposed a novel plan for financing the structure. Mr. Abrams called me and I arranged to go to New York with Mr. Fisher and Mr. Lawrence A. Rubin, our most able secretary, on November 11, 1953. Mr. Abrams proposed two series of bonds with first and second liens on the revenues. Inasmuch as difficulty had already been experienced marketing only first lien bonds, there was considerable doubt as to the marketability of the second lien bonds, even though, according to Mr. Abrams' recommendation, they would carry a higher interest rate. Consequently, the Authority was extremely careful and checked as closely as possible all the aspects of Mr. Abrams' plan.

It was decided that Mr. Abrams ally himself in the management of this financing with other investment bankers. Joseph D. Murphy, of Stifel, Nicolaus and Company, had been interested in the proposal and was allied with C. S. Mott, of Flint. The firm had handled successfully a Mackinac Island issue of some years back. Mr. Murphy provided leadership and suggested to the Authority that Allen and Company and Stifel, Nicolaus and Company consider additional underwriters. This was accomplished with the addition of Union Securities Corporation and A. C. Allyn and Company.

On December 8, 1953, the Authority's able Michigan counsel, John H. Nunneley, of Miller, Canfield, Paddock and Stone, and New York counsel Mitchell and Pershing, with Mr. Rubin were in New York. The Authority's finance committee, Mr. Fisher, Mr. Van Wagoner, and I, were in Detroit. Considerable contact with friends and associates in the banking and industrial world had been had. The phones were pretty busy with discussion of details, and the final go-ahead was given the underwriters. The Authority was determined not to fail the third time.

According to the plan as finally worked out by the underwriters and the Authority and their lawyers, the Authority would offer for sale $79,800,000 worth

18

of first lien bonds carrying a 4 per cent coupon. An additional $20,000,000 of second lien bonds with a 5¼ per cent coupon would be held by the underwriters and offered for sale to the public at their discretion.

This offer had to be subject to "public sale" as required by law. Further, it had to be approved by the state Administrative Board. The public notice appeared in legal publications for seven days beginning December 10, 1953.

The Authority appeared before the state Administrative Board on December 15 to explain the entire arrangement with the request that the Board recess until December 17 to adopt a resolution approving the sale of the bonds which would be made at 10 a.m. that morning. The resolution covering this Board action as well as the trust indenture and notice of sale had already been thoroughly studied by representatives of the state treasurer and the state attorney general.

However, at the Administrative Board meeting on December 15, one of the members raised the objection that the financing method was too expensive and that the entire proposition ought to be subjected to a public vote so that the bonds could be backed by the faith and credit of the state, if the vote were favorable. Obviously, such a move was impossible at this late date. Lieutenant Governor Vandenberg, Speaker Van Valkenburg, several Senate leaders, Joseph E. Warner, chairman of the House Ways and Means Committee and many members of the Legislature had always insisted that the financing must be done without issuing state supported bonds. No state supported bond bill could have been passed. It was explained that such faith and credit financing could be voted upon by the public at any time in the future if the project was successful and the bonds refunded at a considerable saving. The Administrative Board agreed to recess until December 17 as requested.

On December 16, Senator Haskell Nichols of Jackson filed a petition with the clerk of the Supreme Court requesting that body to prohibit the Administrative Board from approving the sale of the bonds. In his petition he stated a number of reasons why he thought the entire procedure was illegal. Had this petition been granted and the Administrative Board enjoined from approving the sale, the bridge financing would have been set back for a full year. It would have been impossible to get a decision on the matter until after the first of the year. The authorization for operation and maintenance money previously appropriated by the Legislature would have expired and new legislation would have been necessary. Experience indicated that such legislation would have taken at least three months to pass, if it would have passed at all. By that time, new contracts would have to be negotiated, new financing arrangements made and another construction season would have been lost.

Fortunately, the Authority attorneys and I were in Lansing on the day the aforementioned petition was filed and we had an audience with several mem-

bers of the Supreme Court. The real impact of granting such a petition was explained to the court members. It was further explained that the Authority had no desire to deprive Senator Nichols of his day in court, but merely wished to consummate the sale of the bonds on December 17 as planned. The Authority actually welcomed a court test. It was pointed out that a complete court hearing could be held on the matter between December 17, 1953 and February 17, 1954, the projected date of the delivery of the bonds. If the senator were on legal grounds, then the court could enjoin the Authority from delivering the bonds. If the procedure were legal, then nobody would suffer a damage. The members of the court present agreed with this reasoning. Subsequently, on January 22, 1954 the court handed down a unanimous decision upholding the complete legality of the Authority's position.

On December 17, 1953 at 10 a.m. in Governor Williams' office at the State Capitol, bids were accepted on the sale of the Authority's $79,800,000 worth of Class A 4 per cent bonds and $20,000,000 worth of Class B 5¼ per cent bonds. One bid was received from the aforementioned management group in the amount of $95,858,000. This was accompanied by a certified check for $100,000. The Authority met immediately thereafter and adopted a resolution approving the sale of the bonds. Directly following this meeting, the state Administrative Board convened after a two-day recess and a motion to adopt a resolution approving the sale of the bonds was passed unanimously.

The next problem was the distribution of the bonds by the four underwriting partners. I spoke to large groups of bond dealers in Chicago and New York on January 5 and 6 to interest them in the Mackinac Bridge project. The final day for such dealers to commit themselves was set for Thursday, January 7, 1954. At 5 p.m. of that day only $35,000,-000 worth of bonds had been committed. By the following Monday sales had been made to several insurance companies; the big one was the New York Life Insurance Company, which agreed to purchase $10,-000,000 worth of bonds. The marketing of the entire issue was soon completed. These were hectic days.

On February 17, 1954, the Authority met with the underwriters in the directors' room of the Bankers Trust Company in New York City and received a check from Joseph King, president of Union Securities Corporation, for $96,400,033.33. The slight variation from the bid is due to accrued interest. On the same date, the Authority's contractors were given letters to proceed with construction, and they began mobilizing their equipment.

Merritt-Chapman and Scott Corporation has the contract to build thirty-three marine foundations for a lump sum of $25,735,600. This contract has no provision for escalation of any items of cost, including labor, materials and quantities.

The contract for the superstructure with the American Bridge Division of the United States Steel

Corporation is in the amount of $44,532,900. It protects the Authority against escalation of wage and material prices but not quantities, which on the superstructure can be closely estimated.

These contracts were made before the amount of the bond issue was determined. It is obvious that financial interests could not absorb an issue without firm contracts, within the total authorized issue. They had to know the bridge could be completed with the money borrowed, so the contracts came before the bond bids were asked.

Additional contracts will be let for paving approaches, administration building, toll gates, and electrical equipment. These amount to approximately $5,500,000. The cost of engineering is $3,500,000, bringing the total construction cost to $79,274,250, more or less. Real estate, preliminary expenses, and administration amount to $800,000.

The following statistics list the proportions of the structure:

Length of suspension bridge (including anchorages)	8,614	feet
Length of main span	3,800	feet
Total length of steel superstructure	17,918	feet
Length of north approach (including mole)	7,791	feet
Length of south approach	486	feet
Total length of bridge and approaches	26,444	feet
Height of main towers above water	552	feet
Depth of tower piers below water	200	feet
Number of main cables	2	
Diameter of main cables	24¼	inches

Number of wires in each cable 12,876
Diameter of each wire .... 0.196 inches
Total length of cable wire .... 41,000 miles
Weight of cable, wire and fittings .... 12,500 tons
Total estimated weight of
        superstructure .... 66,000 tons

The ceremonial groundbreaking for the structure took place on May 7 and 8, 1954 at St. Ignace and Mackinaw City, respectively, the two terminal communities for the structure. Mrs. Prentiss M. Brown wielded the shovel on the northside and Mrs. Charles T. Fisher, Jr., did the honors on the south side. The contracts call for completion of the bridge by November 10, 1957.

When completed, the bridge, in more respects than any other bridge, will be entitled to the accolade "the Greatest Bridge in the World." It is by far the longest suspension bridge from cable anchorage to cable anchorage, 8,614 feet, exceeding the next in size, the 6,450 foot long Golden Gate Bridge, anchorage to anchorage, by 2,164 feet. Its main foundations are in deep and often turbulent water. From the west and northwest, seas generated by over 120 miles of clear sweep in high winds dash forty feet up the towers. Foundations go 200 feet down, and towers rise 750 feet from bedrock—552 feet from the water surface, as high as Michigan's tallest building, the Penobscot in Detroit. The entire project is just forty-four feet more than five miles, all without any intervening land surface. Ice floes pushed by heavy winds race through the four-mile wide channel and at times

have piled thirty feet high, and in forty feet of water have often reached the bottom of the Straits.

What will the bridge do? It will reduce the crossing time, including waiting time, from an average of one and a half hours in winter or two and a half hours in summer, to just ten minutes. At present there have been waiting periods as long as nineteen hours during rush seasons with corresponding line-ups of cars as long as seventeen miles on U.S. 27 and seven on U.S. 131. The capacity of the bridge is 6,000 cars per hour compared with 462 cars per hour of the state ferry system. By cutting out as many as a hundred crossings during a twenty-four hour period, it will eliminate the danger of marine collisions between north and south going ferries and the scores of great ore, grain, and coal ships which steam east and west. Its economic effect on the state will be tremendous. But most of all, it will join the two peninsulas. In the words of Representative Morrison when the final bill was passed, "The North and South of the state have long been engaged; they now have a wedding ring!"

All of us, the engineers, the contractors, the courageous high bridge workers and deep foundation men, the Legislature, and the Governor are proud of this stupendous undertaking. We in the Authority are proud, too. We feel like the pioneer railroad builder who when asked, "What do you like best to do in life," replied, "Plan some big piece of helpful work that everybody says can't possibly be done, and then jump in with both feet and do it."

Designed by Peter Gilleran

Text set in Metrolite by the Jackson Typesetting Co.,
Jackson, Michigan

Engravings by Detroit Gravure Corporation

Printed on India Beckett Text by
Esterling Printing Company, Detroit

Cover, Hamilton Victorian

Bound by Commercial Bindery, Inc., Detroit